Changing Climates
and Natural Habitats

商務印書館(香港)有限公司
http://www.commercialpress.com.hk

CENGAGE
Learning™

Australia • Brazil • Japan • Korea • Mexico • Singapore • Spain • United Kingdom • United States

Changing Climates and Natural Habitats 地球村氣候追蹤

Director of Content Development:
Anita Raducanu
Series Editor: Rob Waring
Editorial Manager: Bryan Fletcher

Associate Development Editors:
Victoria Forrester, Catherine McCue
責任編輯：黃家麗

出版：

商務印書館（香港）有限公司
香港筲箕灣耀興道3號東匯廣場8樓

Cengage Learning
Units 808-810, 8th floor,
Tins Enterprises Centre,
777 Lai Chi Kok Road, Cheung Sha Wan,
Kowloon, Hong Kong

網址：http://www.commercialpress.com.hk

http://www.cengageasia.com

發行：香港聯合書刊物流有限公司
　　　香港新界大埔汀麗路36號中華商務
　　　印刷大廈3字樓

印刷：中華商務彩色印刷有限公司
版次：2010年3月第1版第2次印刷

ISBN: 978-962-07-1876-2

出版說明

本館一向倡導優質閱讀，近年連續推出以"Q"為標誌的優質英語學習系列(*Quality English Learning*)，其中《Black Cat 優質英語階梯閱讀》，讀者反應令人鼓舞，先後共推出超過60本。

為進一步推動閱讀，本館引入Cengage 出版之*Footprint Library*，使用*National Geographic*的圖像及語料，編成百科英語階梯閱讀系列，有別於Black Cat 古典文學閱讀，透過現代真實題材，百科英語語境能幫助讀者認識今日的世界各事各物，擴闊視野，提高認識及表達英語的能力。

本系列屬non-fiction (非虛構故事類)讀本，結合閱讀、視像和聽力三種學習功能，是一套三合一多媒介讀本，每本書的英文文章以headwords寫成，headwords 選收自以下數據庫的語料：*Collins Cobuild The Bank of English*、*British National Corpus* 及 *BYU Corpus of American English* 等，並配上精彩照片，另加一張video/audio 兩用DVD。編排由淺入深，按級提升，只要讀者堅持學習，必能有效提高英語溝通能力。

商務印書館(香港)有限公司
編輯部

使用説明

百科英語階梯閱讀分四級，共八本書，是彩色有影有聲書，每本有英語文章供閱讀，根據數據庫如 *Collins Cobuild The Bank of English*、*British National Corpus* 及 *BYU Corpus of American English* 選收常用字詞編寫，配彩色照片及一張video/audio 兩用DVD，結合閱讀、聆聽、視像三種學習方式。

讀者可使用本書：

 學習新詞彙，並透過延伸閱讀(Expansion Reading)
練習速讀技巧

 聆聽錄音提高聽力，模仿標準英語讀音

 看短片做練習，以提升綜合理解能力

Grammar Focus解釋語法重點，後附練習題，供讀者即時複習所學，書內其他練習題，有助讀者掌握學習技巧如 scanning, prediction, summarising, identifying the main idea

中英對照生詞表設於書後，既不影響讀者閱讀正文，又具備參考作用

Contents 目錄

The CD-ROM contains a video and full recording of the text

CD-ROM 包括短片和錄音

Words to Know

This story is about the earth's **atmosphere** and the **weather conditions** that occur there.

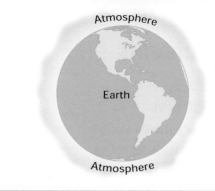

Atmosphere

Earth

Atmosphere

A **Earth and Its Weather.** Here are some types of weather you will find in the story. Label the pictures with words from the box.

hail	snowstorm	tornado
sandstorm	thunderstorm	typhoon

1. _____

2. _____

3. _____

4. _____

5. _____

6. _____

B Predicting the Weather.

Predicting the Weather. Read the paragraph. Complete the sentences with the correct form of the underlined words.

Predicting the weather on the planet is a science known as <u>meteorology</u>. <u>Meteorologists</u> study the earth's atmosphere. Moving air masses in the atmosphere, or <u>fronts</u>, often cause changes in the weather. Meteorologists use devices such as <u>thermometers</u>, <u>radars</u>, and <u>satellites</u> to make <u>predictions</u> about fronts and other weather factors. They always want to be accurate. Many people listen to the weather <u>forecast</u> to plan their day.

1. A _____ is a scientist who studies the earth's atmosphere.

2. A _____ is a statement about what will happen in the future.

3. A _____ is a device that uses radio waves to locate an object.

4. _____ is the study of the earth's atmosphere and weather.

5. A _____ is a line where warm and cold air masses meet.

6. A weather _____ tells us what will happen with the weather.

7. A _____ is a device that measures the temperature of the air.

8. A _____ is a piece of equipment that sends and receives signals in space.

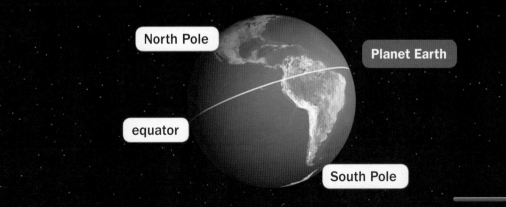

North Pole

Planet Earth

equator

South Pole

ook outside your window. It may be very different to what you saw just a day or two ago. Yesterday may have been cloudy and rainy, today may be beautiful and sunny. But what about tomorrow? Well, you may just want to stay inside!

What is it that causes these changes? It's the weather. Weather is something which we experience every day, and yet it's very **complicated**.[1] Weather is the **temporary**[2] state of the earth's **atmosphere**.[3] It can be very different from place to place at any one time. This is because it depends on the complex relationship between the air, water, and heat from the Sun.

How does the weather work?

---

[1] **complicated:** sth involving so many parts that it is difficult to understand
[2] **temporary:** not lasting
[3] **atmosphere:** the layer of gases around the earth

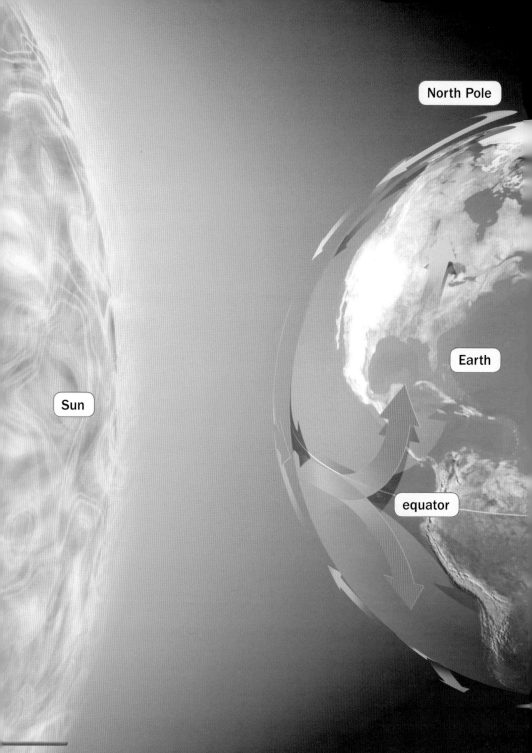

North Pole

Earth

Sun

equator

The weather depends on the movement of the earth, and the earth itself is a **planet**[1] that is always changing and moving. Its atmosphere is like a vast weather engine – an engine that gets its power from the Sun.

The Sun heats up more air over the equator than it does at the poles. This causes huge movements of air across the surface of the earth. The warm, **moist**[2] air near the equator rises and flows towards the poles. The cool air from the poles then drops down and flows back towards the equator. This creates a continuous cycle of moving air.

---

[1] **planet:** a large, round object in space that moves around a star
[2] **moist:** slightly wet

Scan for Information

Scan page 7 to find the information.

1. Where does more air heat up?

2. What happens to the warm air?

3. What happens to the cool air?

4. What does this exchange of air create?

South Pole

As this air moves quickly across the earth's surface, it continuously interacts with the land and the sea. These **components**[1] exchange heat and **moisture**,[2] and create the earth's changing weather. That's why we get things like **heat waves**[3] and **hailstorms**,[4] snowstorms and sandstorms, typhoons and tornadoes. All of these are types of extreme, or dramatic, weather.

Fronts can also cause dramatic weather, but what are they?

---

[1]**component:** one of the parts of sth
[2]**moisture:** small drops of water in the air
[3]**heat wave:** a period of time with unusually hot weather
[4]**hailstorm:** a sudden heavy fall of small hard balls of ice

Fronts are an important part of weather forecasts. Fronts are formed when warm air masses and cold air masses come together. These fronts can be cold or warm. A cold front is created when a mass of cold air forces itself underneath warmer, lighter air. The cold air pushes the warm air out of the way. This often brings **dramatic**[1] changes in the atmosphere, such as heavy clouds and violent storms.

Warm fronts happen when a warm air mass pushes cold air forwards. The weather is usually less dramatic during warm fronts. It may get hotter and more **humid,**[2] but rain and thunderstorms may also occur.

---

[1]**dramatic:** very sudden or noticeable
[2]**humid:** when the air is warm and slightly wet

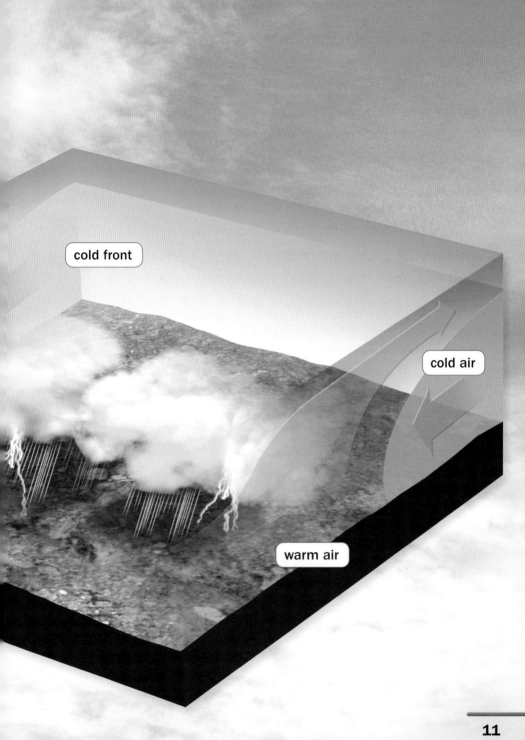

Scientists can often forecast tomorrow's weather by observing and **analysing**[1] the atmospheric conditions today. This science is called meteorology, and it's how the meteorologist on television knows if you should pick up your umbrella, put on some sunglasses, or dress warmly.

Meteorologists, or weather forecasters, watch six key conditions of the atmosphere. These are: air pressure (or the weight of the air above a certain point on the earth's surface); humidity (or the amount of moisture in the air); temperature; clouds; wind; and precipitation (such as rain or snow). Then, they try to make an **accurate**[2] prediction of what the weather will be like tomorrow, or even next week.

---

[1]**analyse:** to examine sth carefully
[2]**accurate:** correct

Of course, it's very useful to be able to know what the weather will be like in the future. But how is it done? Simple devices like **barometers**[1] and thermometers, or more complicated ones like **radars**[2] and **satellites**,[3] are used to measure weather conditions. This data is then used to predict different types of weather.

By measuring a rise in air pressure, for example, barometers can generally tell you to plan for nice weather. If the air pressure drops, there may be storms. Barometers are one way that you can forecast the weather yourself, without the help of a meteorologist. Many people have them at home.

---

[1] **barometer:** an instrument that measures air pressure
[2] **radar:** a system that uses radio signals to find out the position of sth
[3] **satellite:** an object that is sent into space to travel around the earth to receive and send information

Predict

Answer the questions. Then scan page 17 to check your answers.

1. How many thunderstorms occur every day around the world?

2. In what order do these events happen during a thunderstorm? (Number 1-4)

   _____ air cools and ice or water forms

   _____ moisture gets heavy and falls to the earth as rain

   _____ humid air moves upwards

   _____ clouds form

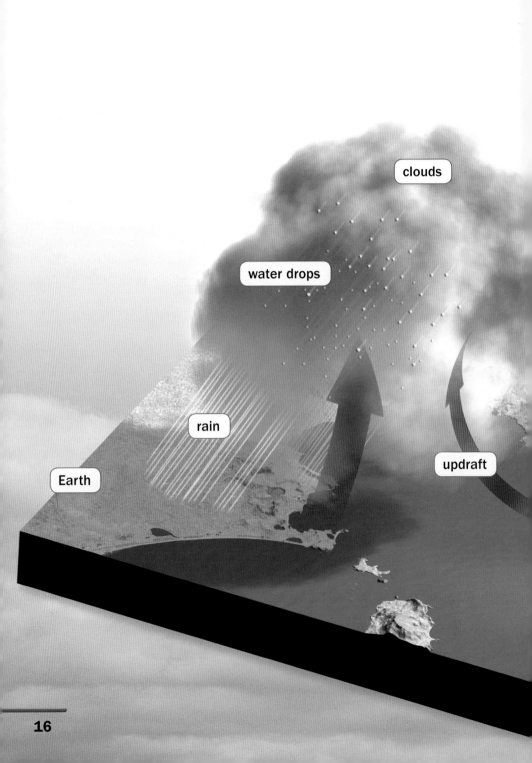

clouds

water drops

rain

Earth

updraft

Thunderstorms are one of the most common forms of extreme weather. About 45,000 thunderstorms occur every day around the world. They usually begin with warm, humid air moving upwards. This is called an 'updraft'. These updrafts rise above the earth and form clouds. Then, ice crystals or water drops form in the clouds as the air cools. Finally, this moisture becomes heavy and falls to the earth as rain.

However, it's not always just rain. If the air temperature is very cold, the moisture can become snow. It can also become hail or **sleet,** [1] depending on the temperature.

---

[1]**sleet:** frozen rain; a mixture of snow and rain

We may not always be happy about the weather, but everyone needs weather forecasts. They help us to plan our daily lives. Farmers depend on accurate forecasts to tell them when to plant and **harvest**[1] crops. Airlines need to consider weather conditions so that their planes can reach their destinations quickly and safely. And you? Well, a good understanding of the weather might help you to decide whether you should go out tomorrow …
or not.

[1]**harvest:** gather fruits, vegetables, or other foods

After You Read

1. Weather can change at _____ time.
   A. no
   B. any
   C. the
   D. some

2. On page 4, the phrase 'temporary state' describes something that is:
   A. never changing
   B. always the same
   C. complex
   D. always changing

3. The weather depends on the _____ relationship between air, water, and the heat from the Sun.
   A. simple
   B. different
   C. complicated
   D. experienced

4. Warm, moist air near the poles rises towards the equator.
   A. True
   B. False
   C. Not in text

5. Which of the following is an appropriate heading for page 9?
   A. Air Interacts with Sea and Land to Change Weather
   B. Air Never Interacts with the Land
   C. Weather Is Always Extreme
   D. Moisture Creates Earth's Changing Weather

6. On page 10, the word 'it' in the second paragraph refers to:
   A. a warm air mass
   B. a thunderstorm
   C. a warm front
   D. the weather

7. Fronts are _____ important part of weather forecasts.
   A. two
   B. all
   C. an
   D. the

8. Barometers measure air pressure.
   A. True
   B. False

9. If the air pressure rises, you will probably:
   A. pick up an umbrella.
   B. put on a jumper.
   C. put on sunglasses.
   D. dress more warmly.

10. Which of the following are <u>not</u> part of the six key conditions of the atmosphere that weather forecasters use to make predictions?
   A. humidity
   B. fronts
   C. air pressure
   D. temperature

11. According to page 17, which of the following statements is true?
   A. Thunderstorms are very rare.
   B. Sleet is a mixture of snow and rain.
   C. Moisture always falls to the earth as rain.
   D. Updrafts are always formed from cool air.

12. The main idea of page 18 is:
   A. only airlines and farmers need forecasts.
   B. only farmers need forecasts.
   C. airlines don't need forecasts.
   D. meteorology is useful for everyone.

Global Warming

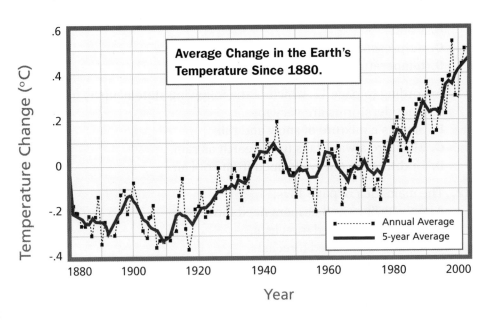

The average temperature on the earth's surface constantly goes up and down. These changes are most often the result of differences in the amount of heat from the sun or natural changes in the atmosphere. It usually takes thousands of years for the temperature to change by even one degree Celsius. However, recent measurements show that the earth's temperature may have increased by almost this much in only the past 100 years. Some scientists believe that this rapid temperature change is the result of human, not natural, activity. The name for this kind of unusual change is 'global warming', and some scientists and meteorologists predict that it may cause serious problems around the world in the near future. Some even believe these problems are already beginning to occur.

Average Change in the Earth's Temperature Since 1880.

Temperature Change (°C)

.6
.4
.2
0
-.2
-.4

1880 1900 1920 1940 1960 1980 2000

Year

■--------■ Annual Average
━━━━━ 5-year Average

'One prediction is that by the year 2100, sea levels will be three feet higher than they are today.'

While not all meteorologists and scientists agree that global warming is a reality, those who do agree have some serious concerns. They expect an increase in heat waves along with extremely heavy thunderstorms and floods in the near future. Some also predict that snowstorms will become more frequent and intense as global warming causes the level of moisture in the air to rise. In addition, others predict that the size and strength of hurricanes and typhoons will increase as ocean temperatures rise.

These scientists also emphasise that people living in cities near the ocean or on small islands should be particularly concerned. They suggest that, as the earth's temperature increases, the ice at the North and South Poles will begin to melt and cause sea levels to rise. This rise in the world's oceans will, in turn, cause coastal flooding. One prediction is that by the year 2100, sea levels will be three feet higher than they are today. This would mean that cities like Venice in Italy, and Miami in the U.S. could lose significant amounts of land to the ocean. Although these are only predictions, governments in most major countries are beginning to take them seriously.

Word Count: 327
Time: _____

Words to Know

This story is set in Africa. It happens in the countries of Congo and Gabon, in an area called the Congo Basin.

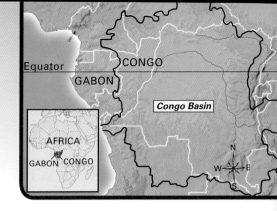

 An Expedition. Read the paragraph. Then match each word with the correct definition.

   This story is about an expedition that travels through parts of Congo and Gabon. The trip starts just north of the equator. The leader of the trip, Michael Fay, works for the Wildlife Conservation Society. His team's aim is to document the wildlife of this beautiful and completely natural part of the world. They must do this before this natural beauty disappears and is lost forever. The biggest challenge for the group will be to cross the varied, and sometimes dangerous, landscape of the Congo Basin.

1. expedition _____

2. the equator _____

3. conservation _____

4. wildlife _____

5. disappear _____

6. challenge _____

7. landscape _____

a. animals and plants that live in natural conditions

b. an imaginary line around the centre of the earth

c. a difficult task that tests someone's skill or will

d. the features of a land area

e. the protection of plants, animals, or natural areas

f. a journey organised for a special purpose

g. to go away suddenly and not return

B **Wildlife in a Wild Land.** Here are some land formations you will read about. Write the correct word next to each formation.

hills	ocean	rain forest	rapids

4. _____

1. _____

2. _____

An Expedition

3. _____

Distances
1 kilometre = 0.62 miles
1 metre = 3.3 feet

It's September in the Congo. Here, just north of the equator, an expedition unlike any other is about to begin. A team of scientists and **researchers**[1] will travel almost 2,000 kilometres through a rain forest in the middle of Africa. This, however, isn't just any rain forest. This one covers over 150,000 square kilometres.

There has never been an expedition quite like this before. The aim of the expedition is to make a scientific record of the unusual and special world of the Congo Basin; a world which could be disappearing.

---

[1]**researcher:** a person whose work is to study a subject in detail in order to discover new facts

Dr Michael Fay is a scientist from the Wildlife Conservation Society. He is leading the group. He calls the expedition 'The Megatransect', or 'the big crossing'. The expedition will go all the way across the Congo Basin. He and his team will travel 2,000 kilometres through the rain forests of Congo and Gabon.

The **conservation**[1] of this rain forest is very important to Fay. He feels the area is a very special place that's disappearing. He says that if they don't document the wildlife here now, there may never be another chance to do it. Fay explains in his own words: 'What I'm trying to do, in a **desperate**[2] way, is to show the world that we're just about to lose the last little **gem**[3] in the African **continent**.[4] And if we don't do something now … if we don't do it today, we can forget about it.'

---

[1]**conservation:** the protection of sth from damage
[2]**desperate:** having an immediate, very strong need
[3]**gem:** a jewel; a very valuable thing
[4]**continent:** one of the main land areas on the earth

Infer Meaning

1. Why does Fay feel 'desperate'?

2. What does Fay mean when he says 'we can forget about it'?

The Congo Basin is one of the world's most important natural areas. It contains almost one quarter of the world's rain forests. It may also have up to half of all of the wild plants and animals found in all of Africa.

Fay's plan is to collect and record information on almost every part of the rain forest. He plans to do this by walking all the way through the forest. During this time, he wants to document the trees, the plants, and the animals that he sees there. It's a big job and it's going to take a long time.

After months of travelling, the team is now in Gabon. Their next challenge is to reach a group of strange hills that are made of stone. These hills rise far above the forest floor.

The men reach the base of the hills. They slowly begin to walk up. Suddenly, they realise that they are above the tops of the trees. They have a wonderful view of everything around them!

From the top of the hills, the team can see very far in every direction.

Fay describes what the team can see. 'We can see a long way here, you know … 70 or 80 kilometres in every direction. We can see 360 degrees around.'

In today's world, it's unusual to be in a place where there are no other people. Fay also **points this out**.[1] 'There are no humans,' he says. 'There's not a single village, there's not a single road.' This makes it clear just how special and completely natural this African rain forest really is. 'It's an **amazing**[2] place,' he adds.

---

[1] **point sth out:** to tell sb about sth in order to draw their attention to it
[2] **amazing:** surprising; wonderful

The team continues on their long trip. As they go, they can hear their next challenge before they reach it – **rapids**.[1]

'OK, wow,' says Fay when he sees the Kongou Chutes. These rapids are an important part of the landscape that the team wants to protect. This area is a land of fast-moving water and very old forests. Both of these things are currently in danger because of **logging**.[2] Businesses want to come here. They want to cut down the trees so they can sell them as wood. If this happens, it will be very bad for the animals and plants in the area. It will also be bad for the land itself.

But, right now, the team has a more immediate problem. These rapids are very fast and very dangerous! According to Fay's plan, the team must cross the river here. Will they be able to cross safely? If they do, how will they do it?

---

[1] **rapids** (noun): a dangerous part of a river where the water flows very fast
[2] **logging**: the work or industry of cutting trees

Predict

Answer the questions. Then scan page 38 to check your answers.

1. How will the team cross the dangerous rapids?

2. What will they need to do it?

The crossing is only a few hundred metres wide, but getting across it is not an easy task. The team members have a lot of experience. They use **guide ropes**,[1] **stepping stones**,[2] and everything they know to get across the dangerous waters safely.

After a lot of hard work, everyone finally makes it across the rapids. It takes the team a full day to get themselves and their supplies across the rapids, and they still have a very long way to go!

---

[1]**guide rope:** a thick cord that people follow to find a way
[2]**stepping stone:** small stones, usually in water, that people walk on

stepping stones

guide rope

After more than a year, the team finally reaches the end of their travels. They are at the Atlantic Ocean, and they are all very pleased to be there. Later, Fay describes how he felt as he took those final steps through the rain forest. 'We'd been walking in the woods in our own little world for 15 months and now it's over,' he says. 'I was **overwhelmed**.'[1]

In the end, Dr Michael Fay and his team walked 2,000 kilometres through some of the wildest lands in Africa. Along the way, they documented as many of the things they found as possible. They did it all as part of the challenging scientific expedition called 'The Megatransect'. They also did it in an **attempt**[2] to save a disappearing world.

---

[1]**overwhelmed:** having a very strong feeling
[2]**attempt:** trying to do sth

After You Read

1. Compared to other rain forests, the Congo Basin is:
    A. small.
    B. a normal size.
    C. dark.
    D. large.

2. What is the main purpose of the expedition?
    A. to study and record what the group see
    B. to walk a long way through the rain forest
    C. to disappear from the earth
    D. to meet new people in the rain forest

3. On page 26, 'one' in the first paragraph refers to:
    A. a country
    B. a rain forest
    C. a scientist
    D. a kilometre

4. Dr Michael Fay thinks the Congo Basin is unimportant.
    A. True
    B. False

5. On page 30, the word 'contains' in the first paragraph can be replaced by:
    A. collects
    B. has
    C. records
    D. takes

6. The Congo Basin has _____ of the wild plants found in Africa.
    A. all
    B. one or two
    C. none
    D. many

7. What will Dr Fay document during his expedition?
   A. wildlife
   B. people
   C. villages
   D. megatransects

8. What is a good heading for page 32?
   A. A View of Everything
   B. No Animals, No Villages
   C. Team Can See a Short Way
   D. Low Stone Hills

9. On page 35, the word 'describes' can be replaced by:
   A. asks
   B. explains
   C. wonders
   D. believes

10. On page 36, who is 'they' in 'They want to cut'?
   A. the expedition
   B. the megatransect
   C. logging businesses
   D. the Kongou Chutes

11. What does the team use to cross the rapids?
   A. stepping stones
   B. guide ropes
   C. experience
   D. all of the above

12. Crossing the Kongou Chutes is a _____ task.
   A. slow
   B. simple
   C. quick
   D. safe

The Wildlife Conservation Society
WHAT IS IT?

The goal of the Wildlife Conservation Society (WCS) is to protect a wide range of animals. Some of the world's animals are endangered, or currently in danger of disappearing. The WCS is also involved in the protection of animal environments. Saving these areas of natural land will allow certain animals to live and increase in number. This work is becoming increasingly difficult. Humans are taking over more of the places where animals used to live.

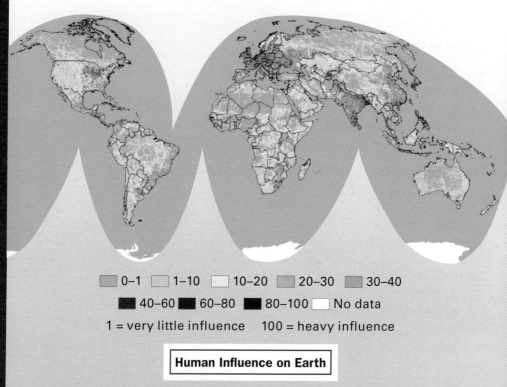

- 0–1
- 1–10
- 10–20
- 20–30
- 30–40
- 40–60
- 60–80
- 80–100
- No data

1 = very little influence   100 = heavy influence

Human Influence on Earth

Source: World Wildlife Fund/U.S. Conservation Science Programme

The WCS works in four major areas:

SCIENCE

Over a hundred years ago, the WCS added its first animal specialist, Dr Reid Blair, to its staff. Since then, the WCS Wildlife Science Division has become a world leader in this field. Today, these study and research activities help to care for more than 17,000 animals in parks around the world.

INTERNATIONAL CONSERVATION

Humans now live on most parts of the earth. People must carefully consider how to best use the few untouched areas that remain. They must also give special consideration to endangered animals. The WCS 'Land Conservation' programme concentrates on these areas.

EDUCATION

The 'Living Landscapes' programme is just one way the WCS helps to protect endangered animals. It provides parks where endangered animals can live safely, which is an important first step. However, animals don't know

> ## 'Humans are taking over more of the places where animals used to live.'

where these parks end. Therefore, local people must also learn how to treat the animals outside of the park area. The 'Living Landscapes' programme helps to educate local communities.

CITY WILDLIFE PARKS

Since 1895, the main WCS office has been in the largest park in New York. School children visit city parks every day of the week to learn about conservation. Several programmes are available in the park system, including family events, discovery centres where people can experience the wildlife, and wildlife theatres.

Word Count: 304
Time: _____

Words to Know

This story is set in Africa, in the country of Tanzania. It is about a mountain called Mount Kilimanjaro.

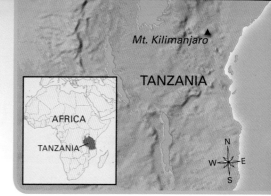

 The Snows of Kilimanjaro. Read the paragraph. Then match each word or phrase with the correct definition.

Mount Kilimanjaro is in a hot, tropical region of Africa. It's only a short distance from the equator. It's the highest mountain in Africa and, even though the nearby areas are hot, the mountain's top is covered with glaciers and large ice fields. The peak is very high so it is cool enough to have ice and snow. Recently, however, there has been less ice and snow on Kilimanjaro. Many people think that this is happening due to climate change.

1. tropical region _____

2. equator _____

3. glacier _____

4. peak _____

5. climate change _____

a. a large mass of ice which moves slowly

b. the highest point on a mountain

c. a hot and sometimes wet area of the world

d. the variation in the earth's global weather over time

e. an imaginary line around the exact middle of the earth

glaciers

peak

Mount Kilimanjaro

Climate Change. Read the definitions. Then complete the paragraph with the correct form of the words or phrases.

global warming: an increase in world temperatures caused by gases that stop heat from escaping into space

ice cap: a large mass of ice that covers a particular area

melt: turn from something solid into something soft or liquid

satellite: a piece of equipment that travels through space receiving and sending signals or collecting information

source: the place where something comes from

There are many causes of climate change. One of these causes, known as (1)_____, may be directly affecting Mount Kilimanjaro. As the earth has got warmer, the ice and snow on Kilimanjaro have (2)_____. Photographs from a (3)_____ in space show how bad the problem is. Much of the (4)_____ at the top of the mountain has disappeared in the last few years. This is a big problem, because the mountain's snow and ice are an important water (5)_____ for the people in the area.

a satellite

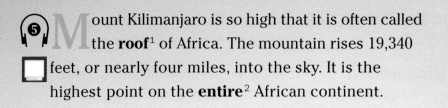

Mount Kilimanjaro is so high that it is often called the **roof**[1] of Africa. The mountain rises 19,340 feet, or nearly four miles, into the sky. It is the highest point on the **entire**[2] African continent.

Mount Kilimanjaro is in northeastern Tanzania, which is in East Africa. It lies almost exactly between the two cities of Cairo, Egypt, to the north and Cape Town, South Africa, to the south. It is around 220 miles south of the equator and in a hot, tropical region of the world.

---

[1] **roof:** the covering that forms the top of a building; top
[2] **entire:** whole

Scan for Information

Scan pages 51 to 55 to find the information.

1. Who wrote a famous story about Kilimanjaro?

2. How long ago were the glaciers on Kilimanjaro formed?

3. What percentage of ice and snow has disappeared from Kilimanjaro since 1912?

4. How long has NASA been taking satellite pictures of Kilimanjaro?

The impressive snow-covered peaks of Kilimanjaro have been an **inspiration**[1] to visitors for a very long time. Over the years, thousands of people have travelled to Tanzania to climb this **majestic**[2] mountain. Many others have come to view its famous glacier-covered peak.

One of these visitors was a famous American writer named Ernest Hemingway. He wrote a story about the mountain that made it famous. The story, first published in 1936, is called 'The Snows of Kilimanjaro'. In the story, Hemingway describes the mountain's ice fields as 'wide as all the world', 'great', 'high', and 'unbelievably white in the sun'.

---

[1]**inspiration:** sb or sth that makes a person work hard or be creative
[2]**majestic:** very beautiful or powerful in a way that people respect

Ernest Hemingway

As Hemingway wrote, the ice fields on Mount Kilimanjaro are certainly impressive. Although the ice cap is **fantastic**[1] to see, it does in fact have a much more important purpose. The glaciers on the mountain were formed more than 11,000 years ago. They have become a very important source of water for drinking and farming for people who live in the areas around Kilimanjaro.

Unfortunately, for the last hundred years, the snows of Kilimanjaro have been disappearing. This has put this essential water source and beautiful sight at risk. Some of the beautiful snows of Kilimanjaro are now missing. But just how much snow has gone?

---

[1]**fantastic:** extremely good

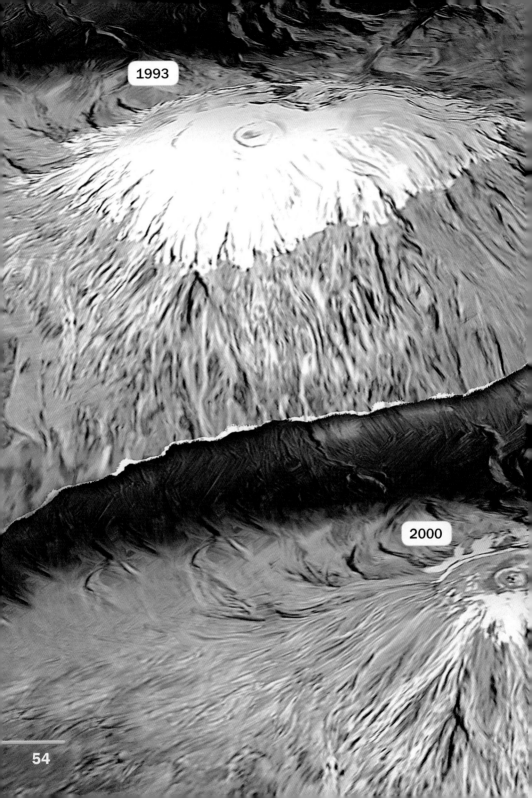

1993

2000

Since 1912, Kilimanjaro's glaciers have got more than 80 percent smaller. The significant changes that are happening on the mountain are becoming more and more **apparent**.[1] A **NASA**[2] satellite has been taking pictures of the mountain's ice cap for more than 15 years. The pictures that the satellite took of Kilimanjaro in 1993 are extremely different from those that were taken only seven years later, in the year 2000. They indicate that there have been very big changes on the mountain. There has been a great **reduction**[3] in the amount of ice in Kilimanjaro's ice cap.

---

[1] **apparent:** clear and obvious
[2] **NASA (National Aeronautics and Space Administration):** a U.S. organisation that is responsible for space travel and the scientific study of space
[3] **reduction:** making sth smaller

The Effects of Climate Change on Kilimanjaro

There are many different ideas about why Kilimanjaro's snow is disappearing so quickly. For one thing, the mountain is in a tropical region, so the glaciers are particularly at risk of the negative effects of climate change. One type of climate change that may be directly affecting Kilimanjaro is called global warming. This worldwide problem is causing a **gradual**[1] increase in the earth's temperature. As the world's temperatures rise, the snows melt.

---

[1]**gradual:** slow and continuous

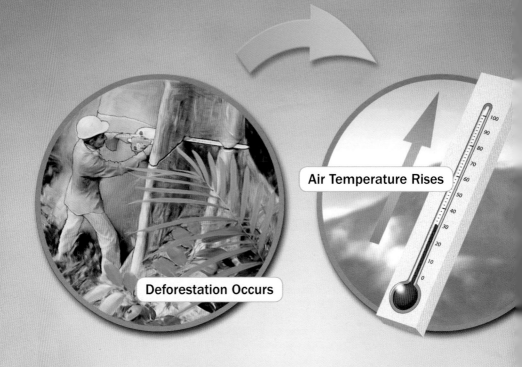

Deforestation Occurs

Air Temperature Rises

How Deforestation Affects Kilimanjaro

Atmosphere Becomes Dryer

Snow Melts

Deforestation[1] is another possible reason why Kilimanjaro's glaciers are melting. When trees are cut down in large numbers, the effects can cause changes in the atmosphere and the climate. Trees keep the air cooler and help maintain the water levels in the atmosphere. This helps to create clouds and precipitation[2] in the form of rain or snow. If there are fewer trees, then this process is affected. The reduced levels of precipitation and increased temperatures can damage the glaciers.

---

[1]**deforestation:** the cutting down of trees in a large area
[2]**precipitation:** water that comes from clouds such as rain or snow

Whatever the causes may be, the snows of Kilimanjaro are continuing to melt at a very fast rate. Experts now predict that the mountain's glaciers could completely disappear by the year 2020.

The loss of Kilimanjaro's glaciers would likely cause many problems for the area around the mountain as well as for the earth. It would remove an important source of water for the people who live on or near the mountain. It could also reduce the number of tourists who come to Tanzania to see the beautiful peak. This would also reduce the amount of money that tourists bring to the country. These changes could eventually have serious effects on Tanzania.

Identify Cause and Effect

Circle the cause and underline the effect in each of the sentences.

1. Because Mount Kilimanjaro is in a tropical region, its glaciers are particularly at risk from global warming.

2. Deforestation often results in changes to the atmosphere.

3. Kilimanjaro's glaciers may disappear by 2020 because the ice caps are melting so fast.

In the end, the missing snows of Mount Kilimanjaro may be a warning. They definitely show people all over the world the dangers of climate change and deforestation. They also show how quickly nature can react and change as a result of these dangers.

Hopefully people will learn from the loss of Kilimanjaro's ice cap. Earth's **natural riches**[1] may not always be around. If these environmental problems are not corrected, we may lose them. Sadly, the majestic snows of Kilimanjaro that so impressed Hemingway may not be available for the world to enjoy forever.

---

[1]**natural riches:** things that exist naturally in large quantities and that are valuable

After You Read

1. Kilimanjaro is called the roof of Africa because:
   A. it covers the whole continent.
   B. it's the biggest mountain in Kenya.
   C. it's the highest point.
   D. the top is tropical.

2. Ernest Hemingway's description of Kilimanjaro shows he:
   A. was amazed.
   B. was scared.
   C. hated it.
   D. was shocked.

3. On page 52, 'they' refers to:
   A. farmers
   B. ice fields
   C. animals
   D. mountains

4. What essential source do local people get from the mountain?
   A. ice
   B. soil
   C. snow
   D. water

5. What's the purpose of page 55?
   A. to explain how a satellite works
   B. to talk about NASA's environmental efforts
   C. to show the effects of global warming
   D. to introduce a new technology

6. How does Kilimanjaro's location affect the environmental change?
   A. The heat melts the snow.
   B. The tropical weather helps trees grow.
   C. It increases the earth's temperature.
   D. The cold creates more ice.

7. Which is a suitable heading for page 55?
- **A.** Reduction Since 1812
- **B.** Ice and Snow Disappear
- **C.** NASA's Pictures Unclear
- **D.** Glacier Remains Unchanged

8. Why are trees important on Kilimanjaro?
- **A.** They help create rain and snow.
- **B.** They cause deforestation.
- **C.** They stop the ice.
- **D.** They help dry the air.

9. On page 60, 'rate' can be replaced by:
- **A.** distance
- **B.** speed
- **C.** time
- **D.** height

10. In 2025, the glaciers might be:
- **A.** cold.
- **B.** big.
- **C.** gone.
- **D.** small.

11. People should take the changes happening at Kilimanjaro _____ a warning.
- **A.** by
- **B.** as
- **C.** if
- **D.** of

12. What is the purpose of this story?
- **A.** to educate about how the planet is changing
- **B.** to talk about Ernest Hemingway's writing
- **C.** to show how people can help the environment
- **D.** to tell the history of an African mountain

http://www.save*the*earth.com

The **Melting** of the Arctic Ice Cap

Scientists have been measuring the gradual disappearance of glacial ice and ice caps on mountain peaks for many years. Most of them have concluded that global warming is part of the problem. The results of this type of climate change are easy to see in places like Mount Kilimanjaro. There, satellite photos have clearly shown how much snow and ice have disappeared in the last few years. However, the problem is much bigger than that. Scientists are particularly concerned about what is happening in the Arctic region. They are especially worried about what is happening to the huge ice cap that covers the top of the earth: the Arctic ice cap.

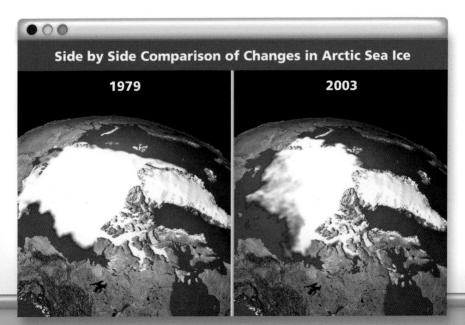

Side by Side Comparison of Changes in Arctic Sea Ice

1979   **2003**

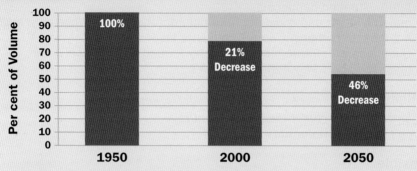

Decrease in the Volume of the Arctic Ice Cap

Per cent of Volume

100%

21%
Decrease

46%
Decrease

1950   2000   2050

This chart shows the percentage of decrease in the size of the Arctic ice cap from the 1950s to now, and the percentage of decrease that scientists predict by 2050.

Temperatures in the Arctic region are rising rapidly – about twice as fast as in other parts of the world. As a result, the ice cap in the Arctic is getting smaller and thinner. Scientists estimate that every year, the Arctic region is losing 9 percent of its ice. At that rate, by the end of the century there may be no more ice left. The Arctic has been covered with ice for at least 50 million years. The effects of a change this large are certain to be felt all over the world.

The Arctic ice melt has already had serious effects on the plants, animals, and native people in the Arctic region. There is much less water for drinking and growing plants. Polar bears and whales have changed their habits. This is making it harder for local hunters to meet their food and clothing needs. The rising level of the sea has forced entire native villages along the coast to move further inland. As the melt continues, countries thousands of miles further south will also be affected. Some scientists predict that sea levels in the United States could rise by as much as three feet by the year 2100. This is something for all of us to think about.

Word Count: 350
Time: _____

Grammar Focus: Future Modals to Express Possibility

- Future modals are formed by *will/may/might/could* + the base form of a verb.
- Future modals are used to express the probability or possibility of a future situation happening.
- *may/might not* and *could not* have different meanings. While *may/might not* means 'perhaps it won't', *could not* means 'it definitely won't'.
- Questions with future modals are only formed with *will: Will it rain tomorrow?* NOT ~~May it rain tomorrow?~~

Definite

It'll be 10 degrees colder there next month.
It won't snow on Wednesday.

Possible

It may rain tomorrow.
I may not go to school tomorrow.

Possible but Less Likely

It might be windy there, so take your jacket.
It might not be very warm on Sunday.
The sun could come out later today.
They could decide to join us at the party later.

Grammar Practice: Future Modals to Express Possibility

A. Write predictions about the weather in your hometown during the times listed below. Use future modals to express possibility.

e.g. next February
It will be cold. It could snow a little. We may not see the sun for a month!

1. tomorrow

   _____

2. next July

   _____

3. next weekend

   _____

Grammar Focus: Future Real Conditionals

Condition	Result
if + subject + present tense verb	subject + will/may/might + verb
If I have time today,	I will call my mother.
If we don't save the rain forests,	we might lose many plants and animals.
If it rains on Saturday,	they won't go to the beach.

- ■ These sentences talk about situations that are real or possible in the present or future. We think they might happen.
- ■ The *if* clause can come first or second in the sentence:
  I will call my mother if I have time today.
  If I have time today, I will call my mother.
- ■ Use a comma after the *if* clause if it comes first in the sentence.

Grammar Practice: Future Real Conditionals: *will, may/might*

Complete the real conditional sentences. Use your own ideas.

e.g. If I have time tonight, *I might watch TV* _____.

1. If we don't stop pollution, _____.

2. If we keep our country clean, _____.

3. If I have enough money, _____.

4. _____, many plants and animals may disappear.

5. _____, our teacher will be really happy.

6. _____, my friends might worry.

Grammar Focus: Adverbs of Certainty

- Adverbs modify verbs or adjectives.
- Adverbs of certainty indicate how sure the speaker is.
- Like other adverbs, adverbs of certainty usually come before the adjective or verb but after the *be* verb or helping verb.

She is <u>definitely</u> happy about visiting Tanzania.
The climbers will <u>probably</u> arrive this afternoon.
We are <u>certainly not</u> coming back here next year.

less certain	more certain	100% certain
possibly	probably (not)	certainly (not)
		definitely (not)
		undoubtedly

Grammar Practice: Adverbs of Certainty
Complete the sentences with an appropriate adverb. Use your own ideas.

less certain	more certain	100% certain
possibly	probably (not)	certainly (not)
		definitely (not)
		undoubtedly

1. I will _____ climb Mount Kilimanjaro some day.

2. Most people _____ know a lot about climate change.

3. I am _____ going to study English tomorrow.

4. People in Tanzania are _____ worried about the disappearing glaciers.

5. I will _____ get a university degree in the next five years.

Grammar Focus: Adverbs of Degree

■ You use adverbs of degree to indicate the intensity of an adjective, verb, or adverb, or to mention the comparative amount of a quality that something has.
■ Like other adverbs, adverbs of degree usually come before the adjective or verb but after the helping verb.
■ Certain adverbs of degree are not usually used with verbs, for example *very, extremely*.

The photos are <u>extremely</u> different from those taken only seven years later.
We <u>barely</u> noticed the scenery because we were <u>so</u> exhausted.

very little

slightly → fairly → rather → quite → somewhat → particularly → very

very much

→ highly → so → extremely → terribly → completely

Grammar Practice: Adverbs of Degree

Match the columns to make correct sentences.

e.g. I hope the glaciers aren't
completely _a_

1. The land there is very ___
2. You hardly ate any of your ___
3. The photographers took ___
4. We nearly forgot to ___

   a. melted when I visit Tanzania.
   b. thank our hosts.
   c. extremely good photos.
   d. dinner. Are you all right?
   e. dry, so deforestation is harmful.

Video Practice

A. Watch the video of *How's the Weather?* and write the word or words you hear.

1. 'This is because it depends on the complex relationship between _____, _____, and _____ from the Sun.'
2. 'Its atmosphere is like a vast weather engine that gets its _____ from the _____.'
3. 'That's why we get things like heat waves, hailstorms, snowstorms, sandstorms, typhoons, and _____.'
4. 'Fronts are formed when warm air masses and cold air masses _____.'
5. 'The weather is usually less dramatic during _____.'

B. Watch the video again and circle the preposition you hear.

1. 'This science is called meteorology, and it's how the weather forecaster (in/on) TV knows ...'
2. 'By measuring a rise in air pressure, for example, barometers can generally tell you to plan (to/for) nice weather.'
3. 'About 45,000 thunderstorms occur each day (across/around) the world.'
4. 'And you? Well, a good understanding (of/with) the weather might help you to decide ...'

Video Practice

C. Watch the video of *A Disappearing World* and circle the word you hear.

   1. 'The Congo Basin contains almost one (quarter/half) of the world's rain forests.'
   2. 'Fay's plan is to collect and record data (in/on) almost every part of the rain forest.'
   3. 'Suddenly, they realise that they're finally (above/near) the tops of the trees.'
   4. 'They can hear their next challenge before they (see/reach) it.'
   5. 'After more than a (year/week), the team finally reaches the end of their travels.'

D. Watch the video again and write the numbers.

   1. 'A team of scientists and researchers is travelling almost _____ kilometres ...'
   2. '... through a rain forest that covers over _____ square kilometres!'
   3. 'We can see a long way here, you know ... _____ or _____ kilometres in every direction.'
   4. 'We can see _____ degrees around.'
   5. 'We'd been walking in the woods in our own little world for _____ months and now it was over.'

73

Video Practice

E. Watch the video of *The Missing Snows of Kilimanjaro* and write down the word you hear.

1. 'Kilimanjaro is in northeastern Tanzania in East _____.'
2. 'It is around 220 miles south of the _____, in a hot, tropical region of the world.'
3. 'Over the years, thousands of people have travelled to Tanzania to climb this majestic _____.'
4. 'Unfortunately, for the last 100 years the snows of Kilimanjaro have been _____.'
5. 'Since 1912, Kilimanjaro's _____ have become more than 80 percent smaller.'

F. Watch the video again and complete the answers to the questions.

1. **Q:** Why is Kilimanjaro's snow melting so quickly?

   A: Because the mountain is in a _____ and because of one type of climate change called _____. _____ is another possible reason.

2. **Q:** What problems would the loss of Kilimanjaro's glaciers cause?

   A: It would remove an important _____ for the people who live on or near the mountain. It could also probably reduce the number of _____ that come to Tanzania.

3. **Q:** What do the missing snows of Mount Kilimanjaro show people all over the world?

   A: They definitely show people all over the world the dangers of _____ and _____.

(1) At any given moment, thousands of thunderstorms are taking place at various locations around the world. **(2)** Approximately 50,000 of them occur every day of the year. **(3)** A thunderstorm occurs when a warm front is joined by a cold front. **(4)** The warm, humid air in the warm front rushes up quickly past the cooler air. **(5)** These updrafts rise high in the sky and form extremely tall cloud masses. **(6)** As the rising air cools, ice crystals or water drops form in the clouds. **(7)** When this moisture reaches a critical point and becomes heavy enough, it falls to the earth as rain or some other form of precipitation. **(8)** Most rainstorms are not dangerous, but some storms – such as typhoons, which form over the ocean, and tornados, which have their origins on land – can be accompanied by highly destructive thunderstorms. **(9)** If the temperature in an area where precipitation is forming happens to be very low, a hailstorm or snowstorm may result. **(10)** Although they are quite rare, large heavy hailstorms can do considerable damage to property, and powerful snowstorms have been known to leave people trapped in their homes for days. **(11)** And then there's sleet – a combination of rain and snow that makes driving a car almost impossible. **(12)** Luckily, today's weather forecasters are able to make fairly accurate predictions about extreme weather conditions, so we can stay safe and comfortable.

A. Read the paragraph and answer the questions.

1. What happens when the moisture in the air reaches a critical point?
   A. The weather gets cold.
   B. An updraft forms.
   C. It begins to fall.
   D. A typhoon forms.

2. What is a good heading for this paragraph?
   A. What Is a Warm Front?
   B. A Big Thunderstorm
   C. How Do Typhoons Form?
   D. Varieties of Precipitation

3. Where should this sentence go?
This difference in temperatures
produces some instant changes.
A. after sentence 2
B. after sentence 3
C. after sentence 6
D. after sentence 8

4. Thunderstorms sometimes form
when a cold front _____.
A. rushes upward
B. becomes colder
C. forms in a cloud
D. meets a warm front

B. Answer the questions.

7. Which of the following does not
occur when the weather is warm?
A. a tornado
B. a snowstorm
C. a typhoon
D. a sandstorm

8. Very small balls of ice are called
_____.
A. snow
B. hail
C. rain
D. sand

5. Which of the following statements
is <u>not</u> true?
A. You will never see clouds near a
typhoon.
B. You need warm air to make
clouds.
C. There are thousands of
thunderstorms happening right
now.
D. Ice crystals sometimes become
rain.

6. In sentence 2, the word 'them'
refers to _____.
A. thunderstorms
B. locations
C. updrafts
D. ice crystals

9. A cold front _____ dramatic
weather changes.
A. may cause
B. should cause
C. won't cause
D. may not cause

10. Which underlined word is
incorrect?
<u>Do</u> you <u>think</u> that it <u>should</u> snow
on Monday, or will the weather
<u>be</u> clear?
A. Do
B. think
C. should
D. be

(1) After eight months of travel, Dr Fay's expedition has reached the rain forests of Gabon. **(2)** They are climbing some hills that rise up hundreds of feet from the ground. **(3)** Suddenly, they realise that they are above the tops of the trees. **(4)** They have a good view of everything around them. **(5)** They can see 70 or 80 kilometres in every direction. **(6)** There are no humans and no roads. **(7)** This shows what a special place the African rain forest is. **(8)** A little later, they reach the Kongou Chutes. **(9)** They must cross these fast-moving rapids. **(10)** The area they are crossing is not very wide. **(11)** However, it takes Dr Fay's team a full day to get from one side to the other. **(12)** A few days later, they have reached the ocean at last. **(13)** They are happy that they have done something to help save the rain forest.

A. Read the paragraph and answer the questions.

11. At the top of the hills, the climbers can see about _____ in every direction.
A. 800 kilometres
B. 8 kilometres
C. 18 kilometres
D. 80 kilometres

12. The Kongou Chutes are _____.
A. fast-moving rapids
B. easy to cross
C. impossible to cross
D. tall hills

13. The writer thinks that the people with Dr Fay are very _____.
A. rich
B. fortunate
C. surprised
D. quiet

14. The word 'they' in sentence 2 refers to _____.
A. the hills
B. the trees
C. the rain forests
D. Dr Fay's team

15. Where should this sentence go?
There aren't any houses either.
  A. after sentence 3
  B. after sentence 6
  C. after sentence 10
  D. after sentence 12

16. The best heading for this
paragraph is _____.
  A. Climbing the Hills of Gabon
  B. Travelling in Africa
  C. Crossing the Rain Forests of
     Gabon
  D. Why We Must Save the Rain
     Forest

B. Answer the questions.

17. An imaginary line around the
earth's middle is called the
_____.
  A. landscape
  B. ocean
  C. equator
  D. rain forest

19. A challenge is _____.
  A. the features of a land area
  B. another word for rapids
  C. a difficult task that tests one's
     skill or will
  D. a kind of rain forest

18. The rain forest will disappear if
people _____ to cut down
trees.
  A. will continue
  B. continue
  C. continued
  D. are continuing

20. If they reach the ocean by Friday,
they _____ happy.
  A. are
  B. will be
  C. were
  D. aren't

(1) Mount Kilimanjaro's appearance is changing. (2) Scientists say that more than 80 percent of its glaciers have melted since 1912. (3) In addition, satellite pictures show that in the seven years between 1993 and 2000, there was a big reduction in the amount of ice in the ice cap. (4) These changes mean that the mountain now looks a lot less impressive than it did 50, or even 10, years ago. (5) Why is this happening? (6) One explanation is that the hot weather in this tropical region increases the effects of global warming. (7) For example, the snow melts much faster here than it does in other, cooler parts of the world. (8) Another reason to explain why the snow may be disappearing is that a lot of the trees on Kilimanjaro have been cut down. (9) This causes the temperature of the air to get warmer and makes the water level in the air lower. (10) These changes cause less snow to fall in the area. (11) Scientists now say that the mountain's glaciers may disappear completely by the year 2020.

A. Read the paragraph and answer the questions.

21. Which statement is true?
  A. Cutting down trees causes a higher water level in the air.
  B. Kilimanjaro looks the same as it did 10 years ago.
  C. Satellite photos show there are now fewer trees on Kilimanjaro.
  D. Cutting down trees helps to make the air in the area warmer.

22. When did satellites show a big reduction in Kilimanjaro's ice cap?
  A. from 1993 to 2000
  B. from 1912 to 1993
  C. from 50 to 10 years ago
  D. from 1912 to the present

23. The word 'this' in sentence 9 refers to _____.
    A. global warming
    B. the melting snow
    C. the low water level in the air
    D. the missing trees

24. The temperatures around Kilimanjaro _____ in the next 10 years.
    A. are likely to higher
    B. are likely to rise
    C. likely will be higher
    D. will rise likely

25. Snow melts faster in the area around Mount Kilimanjaro than it does in some other parts of the world because _____.
    A. Mount Kilimanjaro has a very small ice cap
    B. Mount Kilimanjaro is located in the tropics
    C. global warming doesn't affect other parts of the world
    D. the water level in the air is lower there

26. Cutting down trees _____.
    A. causes clearly the air temperature to rise
    B. clear causes a lower water level in the air
    C. clearly causes the air temperature to rise
    D. causes clearly a lower water level in the air

27. Where should this sentence go? That's 80 percent in less than 100 years!
    After sentence _____

C. Read the sentences. Write 'True' or 'False'. Refer to the paragraph if necessary.

28. A good heading for this paragraph is 'Using Satellites to Record Climate Change'. _____

29. A peak is a large mass of ice that covers a particular area. _____

Key 答案

How's the Weather?
Words to Know: A. 1. hail **2.** thunderstorm **3.** sandstorm **4.** snowstorm **5.** tornado **6.** typhoon **B. 1.** meteorologist **2.** prediction **3.** radar **4.** Meteorology **5.** front **6.** forecast **7.** thermometer **8.** satellite
Scan for Information: 1. over the equator **2.** It rises and flows towards the poles. **3.** It drops down and flows back towards the equator. **4.** It creates a continuous cycle of moving air.
Predict: 1. 45,000 **2.** 3, 4, 1, 2
After You Read: 1. B **2.** D **3.** C **4.** B **5.** A **6.** D **7.** C **8.** A **9.** C **10.** B **11.** B **12.** D

A Disappearing World
Words to Know: A. 1. f **2.** b **3.** e **4.** a **5.** g **6.** c **7.** d
B. 1. hills **2.** ocean **3.** rapids **4.** rain forest
Infer Meaning: (suggested answers) **1.** The rain forest is disappearing. **2.** It will be too late.
Predict: (suggested answers) **1.** They use guide ropes, stepping stones, and everything they know to get across safely. **2.** guide ropes, stepping stones, experience
After You Read: 1. D **2.** A **3.** B **4.** B **5.** B **6.** D **7.** A **8.** A **9.** B **10.** C **11.** D **12.** A

The Missing Snows of Kilimanjaro
Words to Know: A. 1. c **2.** e **3.** a **4.** b **5.** d
B. 1. global warming **2.** melted **3.** satellite **4.** ice cap **5.** source
Scan for Information: 1. Ernest Hemingway **2.** more than 11,000 years ago **3.** 80 percent **4.** more than 15 years

Identify Cause and Effect: 1. Because Mount Kilimanjaro is in a tropical region, its glaciers are particularly at risk from global warming.

2. Deforestation often results in changes to the atmosphere.

3. Kilimanjaro's glaciers may disappear by 2020 because the ice caps are melting so fast.

After You Read: 1. C **2.** A **3.** B **4.** D **5.** C **6.** A **7.** B **8.** A **9.** B **10.** C **11.** B
12. A

Grammar Practice
Future Modals to Express Possibility: open answers
Future Real Conditionals: open answers
Adverbs of Certainty: open answers
Adverbs of Degree: 1. e **2.** d **3.** c **4.** b

Video Practice
A. 1. air, water, heat **2.** power, Sun **3.** tornados **4.** come together
5. warm fronts **B. 1.** on **2.** for **3.** around **4.** of **C. 1.** quarter **2.** on
3. above **4.** reach **5.** year **D. 1.** 2,000 **2.** 150,000 **3.** 70; 80 **4.** 360 **5.** 15
E. 1. Africa **2.** equator **3.** mountain **4.** disappearing **5.** glaciers
F. 1. tropical region; global warming; Deforestation **2.** source of water;
tourists **3.** climate change; deforestation

Exit Test
1. C **2.** D **3.** B **4.** D **5.** A **6.** A **7.** B **8.** B **9.** A **10.** C **11.** D **12.** A **13.** B
14. D **15.** B **16.** C **17.** C **18.** B **19.** C **20.** B **21.** D **22.** A **23.** D **24.** B
25. B **26.** C **27.** 2, two **28.** False **29.** False

English - Chinese Vocabulary List 中英對照生詞表

(Arranged in alphabetical order)

English	Chinese	English	Chinese
accurate	準確的	inspiration	靈感
amazing	驚人的	logging	伐木(業)
analyse	分析	majestic	壯觀的
apparent	明顯的	moist	濕潤的
atmosphere	大氣層	moisture	水分
attempt	嘗試	NASA (National Aeronautics and Space Administration)	美國太空總署
barometer	氣壓計		
complicated	複雜的		
component	成份	natural riches	天然資源
conservation	(對環境資源的) 保護	overwhelmed	非常感動
continent	大陸	planet	行星
deforestation	砍伐森林	point sth out	指出
desperate	極度渴望的	precipitation	降雨(雪)量
dramatic	戲劇性的	radar	雷達
entire	整個的	rapid	急流
fantastic	極好的	reduction	縮小
gem	寶石/寶物	researcher	研究員
gradual	逐漸的	roof	頂部
guide rope	導向繩	satellite	人造衛星
hailstorm	雹暴	sleet	雨夾雪
harvest	收割	stepping stone	踏腳石
heat wave	熱浪	temporary	暫時的
humid	潮濕的		